Biology 1a — Human Biology

Pages 1-2 — Diet and Metabolic Rate

Q1   A diet containing the right balance of different foods and the right amount of energy.

Q2 a)   Protein is needed for **growth** and **cell repair/ replacement** (in either order).

b)   Carbohydrates provide much of your **energy**.

c)   Fats are needed to **keep warm** and for **energy** (in either order). Other answers are possible.

d)   Vitamins and minerals are needed in **tiny/small** amounts to stay healthy.

Q3 a)   The speed at which all the chemical reactions that take place in your body happen.

b)   proportion of muscle to fat in the body, inherited factors, amount of exercise

Q4   Wendy needs more carbohydrate and protein in her diet because she is more physically active. She needs more protein for muscle development and more carbohydrate for energy.

Q5 a)   The average man is bigger than the average woman and so needs more energy for metabolic reactions and movement. The average man also has more muscle, which needs more energy than fatty tissue.

b)   Cyclists riding in the Tour de France are doing a lot of exercise every day, and active people need more energy. They may also be more muscular than the average man.

Q6 a)   Egg

b)   In 50 g of bread there are (50 ÷ 100) × 60 = 30 g carbs. In 50 g of milk there are (50 ÷ 100) × 10 = 5 g carbs. 30 − 5 = 25 g more carbohydrate in the bread.

c)   Any fruit or vegetable. This would provide vitamins, minerals and fibre.

Page 3 — Factors Affecting Health

Q1 a)   They have an unbalanced diet.

b)   A disease caused by a lack of vitamins or minerals.

Q2   You will be 'fit' if you take regular exercise, but if your diet isn't balanced or you're lacking in a certain nutrient, you will be malnourished.

Q3 a)   (16 ÷ 50) × 100 = 32%.

b)   E.g. bad diet, overeating and not enough exercise.

c)   Heart disease, cancers and type 2 diabetes should be underlined.

Q4 a)   E.g. exercise increases the amount of energy used by the body and decreases the amount stored as fat. So people who exercise are less likely to suffer from health problems like obesity.

b)   E.g. inherited factors can affect a person's metabolic rate or cholesterol level.

Page 4 — Evaluating Food, Lifestyle and Diet

Q1   less, use, less, increases

Q2   Report B is likely to be more reliable as it was published in a reputable journal, probably conducted by an independent researcher, and used a large sample size.

Q3 a)   Burger B is the most unhealthy because it contains a higher proportion of fat (including saturated fat) and carbohydrate than Burger A, and has a higher energy content.

b)   Sharon's lifestyle could increase her risk of obesity. This is because she's taking in a lot of energy by eating Burger B regularly, but not using much energy because she doesn't exercise.

Pages 5-6 — F[...]

Q1   A microorgan[...]

Q2   A molecule t[...]

Q3 a)   true

b)   false

c)   false

d)   false

e)   true

Q4   small, damaging, toxins, poisons, cells, copies, bursts, damage

Q5 a)   Blood clots are used to quickly seal the skin if it's damaged and keep microorganisms out.

b)   The air passages are lined with mucus and cilia to trap and remove the bacteria before they reach the lungs.

Q6 a)   White blood cells can engulf and digest microbes. They produce antibodies to kill invading cells, and also antitoxins to neutralise any toxins they produce.

b)   No — a different antibody is needed to recognise each different species of microorganism.

Q7   If a person is infected with chickenpox again their white blood cells will rapidly produce the antibodies to kill it. So they are naturally immune to chickenpox and won't get ill.

Pages 7-8 — Fighting Disease — Vaccination

Q1   causing damage, will

Q2 a) i)   true

ii)   true

iii)   false

iv)   true

b)   Dead and inactive microorganisms are harmless but the body will still produce antibodies to attack them.

Q3   The children who did not get the disease were in better general health.

Q4   John is protected from infection because his white blood cells can make antibodies to the bacterium a lot quicker than James's can. When John was vaccinated, he was given some inactive tuberculosis (TB) pathogens. These had antigens on the surface. John's white blood cells then learnt to make the antibodies specific to these antigens.

Q5 a)   measles, mumps and rubella

b)   E.g. the risk of catching the diseases decreases if more children are vaccinated.

Q6 a)   They've helped to control lots of infectious diseases that were once common in the UK, so far fewer people catch diseases like polio, whooping cough, measles, rubella, mumps or tetanus.

b)   Any two of, e.g. Some people do not become immune after vaccination. / Others can experience a bad reaction, e.g. swelling at the injection site. / In rare cases there could even be a serious reaction such as seizures.

Pages 9-10 — Fighting Disease — Drugs

Q1 a)   The medicine doesn't kill the virus causing the cold — it just relieves the symptoms.

b)   Colds are caused by a virus and antibiotics only kill bacteria.

c)   Because viruses reproduce using your own body cells, which makes it very difficult to develop drugs that destroy just the virus without killing the body's cells.

d)   Different antibiotics kill different types of bacteria, so a patient needs to be treated with the right antibiotic for it to have an effect.

Q2 a)   9 days

b)   Because doctors usually only prescribe antibiotics for something more serious than a sore throat (to avoid over-prescribing antibiotics).

Biology 1a — Human Biology

Q3 a) 1. Bacteria mutate and sometimes the mutations cause them to be resistant to an antibiotic.
2. So if you have an infection, some of the bacteria might be resistant to antibiotics.
3. When you treat the infection, only the non-resistant strains of bacteria will be killed.
4. The individual resistant bacteria will survive and reproduce.
5. The population of the resistant strain of bacteria will increase.
b) E.g. MRSA
Q4 a) E.g. to prevent microorganisms getting in from the air.
b) The flame kills any microorganisms already on the loop.
Q5 a) i) 37 °C
ii) It starts to decrease in number. The bacteria could be starting to run out of food / toxins could be building up / they could be overcrowded.
b) 37 °C is human body temperature — he may be interested in how bacteria grow in or on people.
c) At 25 °C, bacteria that are harmful to humans grow more slowly / aren't likely to grow — so they're less likely to get out of control and infect someone.

Page 11 — Fighting Disease — Past and Future

Q1 a) Semmelweis asked all the doctors to wash their hands using antiseptic solution when entering his ward. This killed bacteria on their hands and stopped them from spreading infections to their next patients.
b) Doctors at this time didn't know about bacteria, so they couldn't see any clear reason to stick to Semmelweis's method.
Q2 a) The number of deaths has fallen dramatically.
b) i) E.g. by overusing antibiotics.
ii) They're working on developing new antibiotics that are effective against resistant strains.
Q3 a) The new strain could be resistant to antibiotics, so current treatments would no longer clear an infection. It could be a new strain that we've not encountered before, so no-one would be immune to it.
b) A big outbreak of disease.
c) Vaccines use dead or inactive microorganisms to stimulate an immune response and prepare the body for future infection. If the microorganism then evolves and changes, the immune system won't recognise it any more and won't be prepared for an infection.

Pages 12-13 — The Nervous System

Q1 E.g. so they can react/respond to the changes and avoid danger.
Q2 Light receptor cells contain a nucleus, cytoplasm and a cell membrane.
Q3 hearing
Q4 a) Chemical receptor. **Tongue** underlined.
b) Chemical receptor. **Nose** underlined.
c) Sound receptor. **Ears** underlined.
d) Pain receptor. **Skin** underlined.
Q5 a) central nervous system
b) brain and spinal cord
c) neurone/nerve cell
Q6 The information from the receptors in the toe can't complete its normal path through the spinal cord to the brain.
Q7 a) i) fingertip
ii) sole of foot
b) The fingertip. This was the most sensitive part of the body to pressure, so it is likely to contain the most receptors.

c) John and Marc might have been applying different pressures, so any differences the pupils noticed might not have been only due to the number of receptors / John and Marc are different, introducing an extra variable so it was not a fair test.
d) Test each pupil a number of times and find the average. Even better, sometimes prod the pupils with one point and at other times with two. Ask them how many points they feel each time.

Pages 14-15 — Synapses and Reflexes

Q1 a) quickly
b) spinal cord
c) protect
d) without
e) receptors
f) neurones
g) chemicals
Q2 a) Eye A has a smaller pupil than Eye B does. Also accept: Eye A has a bigger iris than Eye B does.
b) Eye A. The pupil has contracted in this diagram to stop too much light entering the eye and damaging it.
c) automatic
d) Automatic responses happen very quickly, so the eye can respond to changes in light intensity as soon as possible. This helps your eyes adjust quickly to dimmer light, and stops them being damaged by sudden bright lights.
Q3 E.g. a reflex reaction happens without you having to take time to think about it.
Q4 a) i) sensory neurone
ii) relay neurone
iii) motor neurone
b) i) electrically
ii) chemically
c) i) effector
ii) It contracts (to pull the finger away).
d) i) synapses
ii) The signal is transferred across the gap by chemicals, which are released when the impulse arrives at one side of the gap. The chemicals diffuse across the gap and trigger a new impulse in the neurone on the other side of the gap.

Page 16 — Hormones

Q1 chemical, glands, blood, target
Q2 a) blood
b) oestrogen
c) FSH
d) glands
e) LH
Q3 Hormones use a chemical signal and nerves use an electrical signal. Responses that are due to hormones happen more slowly and last longer than those that are due to the nervous system. Nerves act on a very precise area, while hormones travel all over the body and can affect more than one area at once.
Q4 a) nervous system
b) hormonal system
c) nervous system
d) nervous system
e) hormonal system

Page 17 — The Menstrual Cycle

Q1 FSH — pituitary gland
oestrogen — ovaries
LH — pituitary gland
Q2 a) 1. Causes an egg to mature in an ovary.
2. Stimulates the ovaries to produce oestrogen.
b) Oestrogen inhibits the production of FSH.
c) It stimulates the release of an egg from the ovary.

Biology 1a — Human Biology

Q3 a) & b)

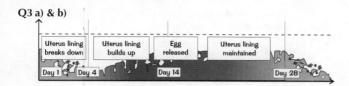

Pages 18-19 — Controlling Fertility

Q1 a) FSH, LH
   b) They stimulate egg release in the woman's ovaries.
Q2 a) E.g. it's over 99% effective at preventing pregnancy. It reduces the risk of getting some types of cancer.
   b) Oestrogen is taken every day to give high levels of oestrogen in the blood. This inhibits the release of FSH by the pituitary gland. Eventually egg development in the ovaries stops so that none are released during the menstrual cycle.
   c) Because it has fewer side effects.
Q3 Reducing fertility — any 2 from: Not 100% effective. Causes side effects like nausea, headaches, irregular periods. Doesn't protect against STDs.
   Increasing fertility — any 2 from: Doesn't always work, causes side effects like abdominal pain, vomiting and dehydration, can result in multiple births, can be expensive.
Q4 The first version of the pill contained high levels of oestrogen and progesterone, but there were concerns about a link between oestrogen in the pill and side effects like blood clots. The pill now contains a lower dose of oestrogen so has fewer side effects.
Q5 a) FSH and LH are given to the woman to increase the number of eggs that develop. The eggs are collected from her ovaries and fertilised outside the body. They're then allowed to develop into embryos. Once the embryos are tiny balls of cells, one or two are then placed back inside the uterus/womb to improve the chance of pregnancy.
   b) **Advantages** — It allows infertile couples to have children. It allows screening of embryos for genetic defects.
   Disadvantages — There can be reactions to the hormones, e.g. vomiting, dehydration, abdominal pain. There may be an increased risk of some types of cancer. The process can be expensive, and there's no guarantee that it will work. It may result in multiple births, which can be risky.
Q6 a) 27.5% (accept 27% to 28%)
   b) IVF treatment is less likely to be successful as the woman gets older.
   c) IVF treatment has a lower success rate in this age group (but is still just as expensive).

Pages 20-21 — Plant Hormones

Q1 a) false
   b) false
   c) true
   d) true
   e) false
   f) true
Q2 shade, faster, towards, lower, faster, upwards
Q3 a) Seedling A: the foil prevents any light reaching the tip, so the auxin is evenly distributed in the tip and no bending occurs.
   Seedling C: the mica strip prevents the auxin from moving to the side that's in the shade, so there is even distribution of auxin and no bending occurs.
   b) E.g. Vicky could repeat the experiment to improve the reliability of the results.
Q4 a) It increased crop yield compared to the field without the weedkiller.

b) Plant growth hormones disrupt the normal growth patterns of broad-leaved plants (the weeds) but not crops. (This kills the weeds and allows the crops to grow bigger as there is less competition for nutrients and light.)

Q5 a)

Concentration of auxin (parts per million)	0	0.001	0.01	0.1	1
Length of root at start of investigation (mm)	20	20	20	20	20
Length of root 1 week after investigation started (mm)	26	32	28	23	21
Increase in root length (mm)	6	12	8	3	1

b)

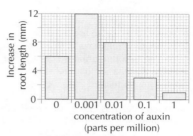

c) 0.001 parts per million
d) High auxin concentration inhibits growth, since the increase in root length is less than when no auxin was added.
e) E.g. He ensured the lengths of all the roots at the beginning were the same.

Pages 22-23 — Homeostasis

Q1 The maintenance of a 'constant internal environment' in the body.
Q2 a) The enzymes controlling all the reactions in the human body don't work as well if the temperature varies too much.
   b) The brain.
Q3 a) The person might have done some exercise. / The person might not have eaten for a long time.
   b) Eating/drinking foods that are rich in simple carbohydrates, i.e. sugars.
   c) To provide the body's cells with a constant supply of energy.
Q4 hot, sweat a lot, less, dark, less, concentrated.
Q5 The following should be ticked:
   Ronald loses salt in his sweat.
   Ronald's kidneys remove salt from his blood.
   Ronald gets rid of salt in his urine.
Q6 a) More water. The exercise will increase his temperature, so he will have to sweat more to cool down.
   b) More water. The exercise will make him breathe harder, so more water will be lost via the lungs.
   c) Less water. More will be lost as sweat and in the breath, so to balance this the kidneys will give out less water in the urine.
Q7 20th July was hotter so she'd sweat more. More water would be lost through her skin and less would be lost in her urine. Her urine would be more concentrated, so the ion concentration would be higher.

Page 24 — Drugs

Q1 a) A chemical that interferes with reactions in your body.
   b) i) Your body can't function normally without the drug, leading to cravings and withdrawal symptoms if the drug is not taken.
   ii) E.g. heroin
   c) To lower the risk of heart and circulatory disease.
Q2 a) E.g. to increase their heart rate.
   b) E.g. the athlete may not be fully informed of the serious risks of stimulants. It makes sporting competitions unfair if an athlete gains an advantage by taking stimulants and not just through hard training.

Biology 1b — Environment and Evolution

Q3 Some studies have shown a link, but others have not. Results can often be interpreted in different ways, depending on what the researcher wants to show (and who's funding the study).

Q4 a) As a control group.

b) Statins combined with lifestyle changes helps to reduce cholesterol levels more than just lifestyle changes alone.

Page 25 — Testing Medicinal Drugs

Q1 1. Drug is tested on human cells and tissues
2. Drug is tested on live animals
3. Human volunteers are used to test the drug

Q2 a) To check whether the drugs have any unknown side effects, and to find the optimum dose of each drug.

b) To make sure the drug has no harmful side effects when the body is working normally.

Q3 a) For use as a sleeping pill.

b) It relieved morning sickness, but it also crossed the placenta and stunted the growth of the fetus's limbs.

c) e.g. leprosy

Q4 a) A placebo is a pill that looks like a drug being tested but contains no drug.

b) They use a placebo to make sure it is the actual drug which is causing any effects. Some patients will have beneficial effects just because they *think* they are receiving medicine.

c) A double blind trial is one where neither the scientist doing the test nor the patient knows whether they are getting a drug or a placebo.

Page 26 — Recreational Drugs

Q1 Liver disease, unconsciousness and addiction should be underlined.

Q2 a) Any two from: e.g. for enjoyment / relaxation/stress relief / inspiration.

b) E.g. they can cause problems with the heart / circulatory system.

Q3 a) Stepping stone — using cannabis makes people want to try harder drugs.

b) Gateway drug — people who use cannabis will have access to drug dealers and so will find it easier to try harder drugs.

c) Genetics — some people are just more likely to use drugs, so people that use cannabis are more likely to use all kinds of drugs.

Q4 a) Because so many more people take them.

b) Any two from: The NHS spends large amounts each year on treating patients with smoking- or drinking-related problems. / The cost to businesses of people missing work due to smoking- or drinking-related problems. / The cost of cleaning up the streets, police time, damage to people and property, etc.

Pages 27-29 — Mixed Questions — Biology 1a

Q1 a) The sense organs are the ears, and they contain sound and balance receptors.

b) i) Sensory neurones carry impulses from receptors to the CNS. Motor neurones carry impulses from the CNS to the effectors (muscles and glands).

ii) The nerve signal is transferred by chemicals that diffuse across the synapse and set off a new electrical signal in the next neurone.

c) i) E.g. to increase muscle size

ii) E.g. high blood pressure

Q2 a) 30 days

b) An egg is released / ovulation.

c) Any from: FSH / LH / progesterone.

d) Oestrogen inhibits the production of FSH, which stops egg development and production.

Q3 a) i) Vitamins

ii) Overeating

iii) higher

iv) more

v) energy

b) i) E.g. through the skin as sweat, via the lungs in breath, via the kidneys as urine.

ii) If the air is hotter then more water will be lost through sweat so less urine will be produced.

Q4 a) To see whether the drug works, to find out its toxicity and the best dosage to use.

b) Whether it is published in a reputable journal, whether it was written by a qualified person, whether it was written by someone who may be biased, how large a sample was used.

Q5 true, false, false, true, false

Q6 a) In the blood.

b) slow response, response lasts for a long time

c) i) At the tips of the shoots and roots.

ii) In shoots, auxin makes the cells grow faster. In the roots, auxin slows cell growth.

iii) e.g. weedkiller

Q7 a) The bacteria have been killed by the antibiotic.

b) i) Antibiotic 3.

ii) No, because flu and colds are caused by viruses but antibiotics don't kill viruses.

Biology 1b — Environment and Evolution

Pages 30-31 — Adaptations

Q1 a) The kangaroo rat.

b) The polar bear.

c) The polar bear has a rounded body shape, which means it has a small surface area for its volume.

d) Less heat.

e) It would be bigger than the polar bear's because the desert is very hot, so the kangaroo rat needs to lose more heat than the polar bear, which lives in a cold climate.

Q2 a) In the desert.

b) i) The cactus has spines instead of leaves, because the small surface area gives less of a surface for water to evaporate from. / The spines help to protect the cactus from being eaten by animals.

ii) The cactus has a thick, fleshy stem where it can store water. / The stem can photosynthesise.

iii) The cactus has shallow but very extensive roots, so it can take in as much water as possible when it rains.

Q3 extremophiles, temperature, pressure (or pressure, temperature)

Q4 a) i) white fur

ii) It provides camouflage (white colour makes it hard to spot against a snowy background).

b) It is a warning colour to scare off predators.

c) E.g. thorns on roses / sharp spines on cacti / the shell of a tortoise / poison in bees / poison in poison ivy.

Q5 a) Reading down the table: 1.5 : 1, 1 : 1, 0.75 : 1, 0.6 : 1.

b) The surface area : volume ratio decreases as the size of the cube increases.

c) The small cube, because it has a small volume where it can hold heat but a relatively large surface over which it can lose it.

d) A mouse is small so it would lose heat quickly. Fur provides a layer of insulation to minimise heat loss.

Biology 1b — Environment and Evolution

Pages 32-33 — Competition and Environmental Change

Q1 a) Light — Plants
Minerals from the soil — Plants
Space — Plants and Animals
Water — Plants and Animals
Food — Animals
Mates — Animals

b) The two species would have to compete for it.

c) E.g. as a source of food.

Q2 a) Any two from: the temperature of the water increased, the amount of light increased, the amount of nutrients increased, etc.

b) The number of fish in the pond increased rapidly in May (also accept April). Even though the water is warm at this time and there is a lot of light, the number of algae suddenly decreases, so this must be because they are being eaten by fish.

Q3 a)

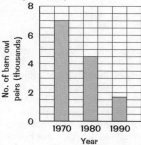

b) There was an overall decline in the barn owl population between 1970 and 1990.

c) Any two from, e.g. loss of habitat, competition from another bird, predation, disease.

Q4 a) The maximum height up the mountain where the snail was found has increased over the last 100 years.

b) The snail species is found higher up the mountain, because it's warmer than it used to be higher up.

c) E.g. average rainfall / air pollution / water pollution

Page 34 — Measuring Environmental Change

Q1 a) True
b) True
c) False

Q2 a) 1970.
b) About 1 million tonnes.
c) lichen

Q3 a) An indicator species.

b) E.g. collect samples of the same size / in the same way / at the same time of day.

c) Mayfly larvae prefer clean water and sludgeworms prefer water that contains sewage.

d) E.g. Sewage is full of bacteria, which use up a lot of oxygen. Animals like mayfly larvae might not have enough oxygen to survive.

Page 35 — Pyramids of Biomass

Q1 a) algae
b) winkle
c) algae/producers

Q2 a) C

b) The total mass of the organisms decreases at each trophic level as shown by this pyramid.

c) Their energy initially comes from the Sun.

Q3 a) The levels of DDT increase dramatically as you go up the trophic levels.

b) i) 13.8 ÷ 0.04 = **345**
ii) 2.8 ÷ 0.04 = **70**

c) DDT is stored in the tissues of animals and a pyramid of biomass represents the mass of the living tissues.

Pages 36-37 — Energy Transfer and Decay

Q1 a) true
b) true
c) true
d) true
e) false
f) false

Q2 Any three from:
Decomposers — Adding more decomposers will speed up decay.
Shredded waste — Shredding the waste gives more surface area for the microorganisms to work on.
Base in contact with soil — More microorganisms will have access to the contents of the compost bin.
Mesh sides — These allow contact with the air, so plenty of oxygen is available to help the microorganisms work faster.
Open top — This allows contact with the air, so plenty of oxygen is available to help the microorganisms work faster.

Q3 a) energy
b) plants, photosynthesis
c) eat
d) respiration
e) lost, movement
f) inedible, hair

Q4 1. Plants take up minerals from the soil.
2. Plants use minerals and the products of photosynthesis to make complex nutrients.
3. Nutrients in plants are passed to animals through feeding and used in respiration to provide energy.
4. Energy released in respiration is lost by decay, heat and movement and the production of waste.
5. Waste and dead tissues are decayed by microorganisms.
6. Materials are recycled and returned to the soil by decay.

Q5 a) i) E.g. carbon, nitrogen, oxygen, hydrogen
ii) From the soil, air, water or eating other plants and animals.

b) When animals die or produce waste, microorganisms cause these materials to decay. The process of decay releases the elements back to the soil, air or water again for plants to use. The plants are then eaten by animals.

Q6 a) not stable
b) stable
c) not stable
d) stable

Q7 a) (2070 ÷ 103 500) × 100 = **2%**
b) 2070 ÷ 10 = 207
207 – (90 + 100) = **17 kJ**
c) E.g. heat loss / movement / excretion
d) So much energy is lost at each stage of a food chain that there's not enough left to support more organisms after about five stages.

Page 38 — The Carbon Cycle

Q1 carbon dioxide, photosynthesis, respiration, microorganisms, eating, carbohydrates, waste, detritus

Q2 Plants use — carbon dioxide to build complex molecules.
Microorganisms release — carbon dioxide by decaying waste and dead tissue.
Animals and plants release — carbon dioxide through respiration.
Animals take in — carbon through feeding.
Plants take in — carbon by photosynthesis.

Q3 a) fossil fuel (accept coal or oil)
b) combustion / burning

Biology 1b — Environment and Evolution

Pages 39-40 — Variation

Q1 have differences, genes, gametes, Identical twins, hair style, environment, variation

Q2 a) No. Identical twins have exactly the same genes. Features like hair colour are controlled by genes, so you would expect the girls to have the same hair colour.

b) The difference in weight must be due to environment (e.g. eating more or exercising less), because the twins have exactly the same genes.

c) I don't think that birthmarks are caused by genes. Identical twins have exactly the same genes, so if Stephanie had a birthmark then Helen should too if it was genetic.

Q3 a) Sexual reproduction gives new combinations of genes, so the foal might not be genetically suited to racing. / Organisms are affected by their environment as well as their genes.

b) Genes.

Q4 a) The lighter moth was better camouflaged against the bark of the trees, so it was less likely to be spotted and eaten by birds.

b) As industry increased, the trees became darkened with soot. Now the dark moths were better camouflaged, so they increased in number.

c) Genes.

Q5 a) These plants have very different characteristics because they are different species and so have different genes.

b) Organisms that reproduce by sexual reproduction receive different combinations of genes, so each organism has its own unique characteristics.

c) The strawberry plants may have been grown in different environments (also accept: The plants may not have had the same parent.)

Page 41 — Genes, Chromosomes and DNA

Q1 nucleus, chromosomes, DNA, genes
Q2 gene, chromosome, nucleus, cell.
Q3 'Alleles' are different forms of the same gene.
Q4 There are two chromosome 7s in a human nucleus, one from each parent.
Q5 a) 2
b) 2
c) 1

Page 42 — Reproduction

Q1 a) two
b) gametes
c) identical
d) half as many
e) Sexual
Q2 a) clones
b) sperm
c) fertilisation
Q3 a) The new skin cells came from the existing skin cells around the cut dividing to give new cells.
b) Asexual reproduction produces cells with identical genes to the parent cells.
c) It took time for the cells to divide enough times to cover the cut completely.
Q4 Sexual reproduction involves the production of gametes by each parent. Each gamete has half the normal number of chromosomes. The gametes fuse together and a baby with a full set of chromosomes is produced.

Pages 43-44 — Cloning

Q1 Parent plant → Cuttings are taken, each with a new bud on → The cuttings are kept in moist conditions until they are ready to plant → Cloned plant

Q2 a) A few plant cells are put into a growth medium with hormones and they grow into new plants / clones of the parent plant.

b) Any two from: e.g. new plants can be made very quickly. / They can be made in very little space. / They can be grown at different times of the year.

Q3 removing and discarding a nucleus = **A**
implantation in a surrogate mother = **D**
useful nucleus extracted = **B**
formation of a diploid cell = **C**

Q4 a) False
b) False
c) True
d) False
e) True

Q5 genetically, nucleus, egg, donor, electric shock, dividing, genetically, donor

Q6 E.g. cloning quickly gets you lots of ideal offspring. But you also get a population with a reduced gene pool — so if a new disease appears, they could all be wiped out. The study of animal clones could improve our understanding of the development of the embryo / of ageing and age-related disorders. Cloning could also be used to help preserve endangered species. However, it's possible that cloned animals might not be as healthy as normal ones. Some people worry that humans might be cloned in the future and any success may follow many unsuccessful attempts, e.g. children born severely disabled.

Pages 45-46 — Genetic Engineering

Q1 a) The purpose of the trial was to see what effect growing herbicide-tolerant GM crops would have on wildlife.

b) i) So that both types of crop experienced the same conditions — otherwise it wouldn't have been a fair test.

ii) Both halves of the fields were ploughed in the same way, and given the same amount of fertiliser etc. This makes it a fair test.

iii) The herbicides were applied differently, because herbicide-tolerant crops and 'normal' crops need herbicide applying in different ways.

c) i) farmers: e.g. if there are fewer weeds to compete with their crops, farmers would have bigger crop yields. This would make them more money. / Farmers may be able to apply herbicide less often/less herbicide overall, saving them time/money.
shoppers buying these products: e.g. if farmers were producing bigger yields, they could afford to sell their products more cheaply. This would save shoppers money. / The products produced would be of a better quality.

ii) The farmers were able to use herbicides that killed a wider variety of weed species on the GM crops.

iii) E.g. the herbicide used on the GM crop allowed more weeds to grow on the GM crop fields than on the 'normal' crop fields. This meant the GM crop fields had more weed flowers, which were able to support more butterflies and bees.

d) i) E.g. yes they do, because most of the GM crops had less wildlife living amongst the plants.

ii) E.g. people are worried that they may not be safe to eat. There are also concerns that transplanted genes may get out into the natural environment.

Chemistry 1a — Products from Rocks

Pages 47-48 — Evolution

Q1

	Plant	Animal
Travels to new places		X
Makes its own food	X	
Is fixed to the ground	X	
May be single celled		

Q2 a) Rays and Sharks
b) E.g. they could be in competition.
Q3 There is variation within species caused by differences in their genes
The best adapted animals and plants are most likely to survive.
Some characteristics are passed on through reproduction from parent to offspring.
Q4 1. Ancestors to the buff tip moth showed variation in their appearance. Some had genes that made them look a bit like a stick.
2. Short-sighted birds in poor light didn't spot the stick-like moths.
3. So the stick-like moths were more likely to survive and reproduce.
4. Genes that made the moths look like sticks were more likely to be passed on to the next generation.
Q5 a) E.g. longer legs would help when running away from predators. B has a hoof rather than toes. This makes it more stable when running. The environment may have changed from rocky slopes or swamps (where toes would help with balance) to flat plains (where balance is less important).
b)

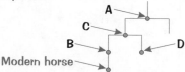

Page 49 — More About Evolution

Q1 A, E
Q2 Lamarck, more developed, longer, the next generation
Q3 People with dyed blue hair do not have children with blue hair.
Sheep whose tails are cut short give birth to lambs with full-length tails.
Q4 Any two from, e.g. because they have different beliefs / because they have been influenced by different people / because they think differently.

Pages 50-52 — Mixed Questions — Biology 1b

Q1 a) i) It increased.
ii) It stayed constant.
b) The goat.
c) Because they lose too much water, and water is scarce in the desert.
d) natural selection
Q2 a) Donkeys have 62 chromosomes and horses have 64 chromosomes, so mules will have 63 chromosomes.
b) Ligers have chromosomes that can all pair up, because lions and tigers have the same number of chromosomes. Mules have one chromosome that can't pair up, so their chromosome pairs can't split up to make normal gametes.
Q3 a) Egg A. The parents of egg A provided the genetic material that was inserted into egg B, so the toad inherited its features from these parents.

b) Dolly was a clone because she was produced using genetic material from a single sheep. The fertilised cell used in the toad experiment contained a mixture of genes from two parents, so was not a clone.
c) E.g. space and food
d) Species that are sensitive to slight changes in their environment (so can be used to indicate environmental conditions).
Q4 a) To check that the gene for growth hormone had been inserted successfully. The piece of DNA that was inserted contained both these genes, so if the bacteria were resistant to the penicillin they would also be able to produce growth hormone.
b) E.g. bacteria reproduce quickly.
c) asexual
Q5 a) i) 43 700 − 7500 = **36 200 kJ**
ii) 7500 ÷ 43 700 × 100 = **17%**
b) E.g. in maintaining a constant body temperature / in waste materials.
c) A — respiration
B — feeding / ingestion / digestion
C — death and waste
D — CO_2 release from decay / respiration by decomposers
E — photosynthesis
F — respiration
d) The high temperature and good availability of oxygen will increase the rate of decomposition, as microorganisms work well in these conditions.

Chemistry 1a — Products from Rocks

Page 53 — Atoms and Elements

Q1 a) zero
b) ion
c) protons, electrons (in either order)
d) negatively
Q2

Particle	Charge
Proton	+1
Neutron	0
Electron	-1

Q3 a) nucleus
b) electron
c) proton
d) neutron
e) proton
Q4

Diagram should be correctly labelled as above
Q5 copper and oxygen should be circled

Page 54 — The Periodic Table

Q1 a) A group in the periodic table is a **vertical** line of elements.
b) Most of the elements in the periodic table are **metals**.
c) There are about 100 different **elements** in the periodic table.
d) Non-metals are on the **right-hand** side of the periodic table.
e) Elements in the same group have **similar** properties.
f) The symbol for chlorine is **Cl** and the symbol for potassium is **K**.

Chemistry 1a — Products from Rocks

Q2 a)

    b)   11
    c)   11
    d)   23 − 11 = **12**

Q3 a)   The following should be ticked: **A** and **D**
    b)   Sodium and potassium are both in Group I, so they both contain the same number of electrons in their outer shell. The properties of elements are decided by the number of electrons they have in their outer shell.

Q4 a)   false
    b)   false
    c)   true
    d)   true
    e)   true

Pages 55-56 — Electron Shells

Q1 a) i)   true
    ii)   false
    iii)   false
    iv)   false
   b) ii)   The lowest energy levels are always filled first.
    iii)   Atoms are most stable when they have full outer shells.
    iv)   Reactive elements have partially filled outer shells.

Q2   E.g. The inner most electron shell should be filled first / there should be two electrons in the inner shell; The outer shell contains too many electrons, it only holds a maximum of 8 electrons.

Q3 a)   2,2
    b)   2,6
    c)   2,8,4
    d)   2,8,8,2
    e)   2,8,3
    f)   2,8,8

Q4 a)   Noble gases are unreactive elements because they have full outer shells of electrons.
    b)   Group I metals are reactive elements, because they have an incomplete outer shell of electrons.

Q5 a)   2,8,7
    b)

    c)   Its outer shell isn't full (it's keen to get an extra electron).

Q6

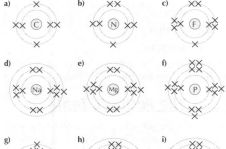

Page 57 — Compounds

Q1 a)   true
    b)   true
    c)   true
    d)   true

Q2   Missing words are: ions, positive, negative, attracted, ionic, molecules, covalent.

Q3 a)   ionic
    b)   1
    c)   +1
    d)   NaCl

Q4   Sharing electrons allows both atoms to achieve the stable 'full outer shell' of electrons. They form covalent bonds.

Pages 58-59 — Balancing Equations

Q1 a)   Correctly balanced
    b)   Incorrectly balanced
    c)   Incorrectly balanced
    d)   Correctly balanced
    e)   Correctly balanced
    f)   Correctly balanced

Q2   The third equation should be circled.

Q3 a)   The reactants are methane and oxygen, and the products are carbon dioxide and water.
    b)   methane + oxygen → carbon dioxide + water
    c) $CH_4 + 2O_2 \rightarrow CO_2 + 2H_2O$

Q4 a) $2Na + Cl_2 \rightarrow 2NaCl$
    b) $4Li + O_2 \rightarrow 2Li_2O$
    c) $MgCO_3 + 2HCl \rightarrow MgCl_2 + H_2O + CO_2$
    d) $2Li + 2H_2O \rightarrow 2LiOH + H_2$

Q5 a) $CuO + \mathbf{2}HBr \rightarrow CuBr_2 + H_2O$
    b) $H_2 + Br_2 \rightarrow \mathbf{2}HBr$
    c) $\mathbf{2}Mg + O_2 \rightarrow 2MgO$
    d) $2NaOH + H_2SO_4 \rightarrow Na_2SO_4 + \mathbf{2}H_2O$

Q6 a) $\mathbf{3}NaOH + AlBr_3 \rightarrow \mathbf{3}NaBr + Al(OH)_3$
    b) $\mathbf{2}FeCl_2 + Cl_2 \rightarrow \mathbf{2}FeCl_3$
    c) $N_2 + \mathbf{3}H_2 \rightarrow \mathbf{2}NH_3$
    d) $\mathbf{4}Fe + 3O_2 \rightarrow 2Fe_2O_3$
    e) $\mathbf{4}NH_3 + \mathbf{5}O_2 \rightarrow \mathbf{4}NO + \mathbf{6}H_2O$

Pages 60-64 — Using Limestone

Q1   calcium carbonate

Q2 a)   calcium oxide, carbon dioxide
    b)   magnesium oxide
    c) $CuCO_3 \rightarrow CuO + CO_2$
    d)   A Bunsen burner would not reach a high enough temperature for the reaction to happen.

Q3   The missing words are: limestone, mortar, concrete.

Q4 a)   calcium carbonate → calcium oxide + carbon dioxide
    b)   To neutralise soils that are acidic.

Q5 a)   carbon dioxide, water
   b) i)   magnesium carbonate + sulfuric acid → magnesium sulfate + carbon dioxide + water
    ii) $MgCO_3 + H_2SO_4 \rightarrow MgSO_4 + CO_2 + H_2O$
    c)   Any two from, e.g. copper/zinc/calcium/sodium
    d)   Limestone is mainly calcium carbonate and acid rain is a weak acidic solution. So, when acid rain falls, it reacts with the calcium carbonate to form a salt, carbon dioxide and water. This means that limestone buildings are gradually eroded away by acid rain.

Q6 a)   If you make a saturated solution of calcium hydroxide in water (called limewater) and bubble gas through it, the solution will turn cloudy if the gas is carbon dioxide.
    b) $Ca(OH)_2 + CO_2 \rightarrow CaCO_3 + H_2O$

Q7 a)   Thermal decomposition is when one substance chemically changes into at least two new substances when it's heated.

b) Calcium oxide will react with water to give an alkaline substance. You could prove this using universal indicator (it would turn blue or purple). Calcium carbonate would remain neutral.

Q8 a) The limestone in the Peak District is very pure.
b) About 1.6 million tonnes (7.9 ÷ 5 = 1.58).
c) It is used in agriculture and burned in lime kilns.
d) Any three from: increased traffic, spoiling the look of the landscape, discouraging tourism, noise, dust, damage to habitats and the environment.
e) i) canals and railways
ii) by road / by lorry
f) Answer will depend on student's opinion, but they are likely to say that they are against it because the article focuses on the problems associated with quarrying rather than the benefits it has.
g)

Use	Percentage	Total amount quarried in tonnes
Aggregate (for road-building etc.)	52%	(7900000 ÷ 100) ×52 = 4108000
Cement	24%	(7900000 ÷ 100) ×24 = 1896000
Iron and steel making	2%	(7900000 ÷ 100) ×2 = 158000
Chemicals and other uses	22%	(7900000 ÷ 100) ×22 = 1738000

Q9 Granite, paint and bricks should be circled.
Q10a) neutralisation
b) The powdered limestone removes sulfur dioxide from the waste gases.
Q11a) Any two from, e.g. it makes huge holes which permanently damage the landscape / noise / dust / destruction of habitats for plants and animals / transport is usually by lorry causing more noise and pollution / waste material causes unsightly tips.
b) Quarries provide employment for local people which can provide a boost to the local economy. There may also be improvements to infrastructure such as roads, recreational and health facilities.
Q12a) Wood rots, is damaged by insects and is flammable. Concrete is not affected by any of these problems.
b) Metals corrode but concrete doesn't.
c) Bricks are made to a set size and shape but concrete can be poured into moulds of any size and shape.

Pages 65-69 — Getting Metals from Rocks

Q1 a) A metal ore is a mineral which contains enough metal to make it worthwhile extracting the metal from it.
b) oxygen and sulfur
Q2 Gold is less common than iron, which makes it expensive and this means that it is worth extracting it from low-grade ores. Iron is less valuable, and more common, so it is only economic to extract it from high-grade ores.
Q3 a) Year 1
b) cost of extraction = 75/100 x £2.00 = £1.50
The cost of mineral extraction was **£1.50** in year 6.
Q4 As technology improves, it becomes possible to extract more metal from a sample of rock than before. So it might now be worth extracting metal that wasn't worth extracting in the past.
Q5 Missing words are: carbon, below, reduction, electrolysis, more.
Q6 dekium, bodium, **carbon**, candium, antium

Q7 a) Any one from:
e.g. it is too impure to conduct electricity well. / The impurities make it too brittle to be used for wires.
b) i) Impure copper (obtained e.g. by reduction with carbon) is purified using electrolysis.
ii) E.g. electrolysis is expensive because it uses a lot of energy.
Q8 Missing words are: electricity, liquid, electricity, positive, electrode.
Q9 Electrolysis is the breaking down of substances using electricity. A molten substance or solution has free ions which conduct the electricity.
Q10 The copper produced will have zinc impurities in it.
Q11a) A — electrodes
B — copper sulfate solution
C — copper ions
b) The impurities are not charged (i.e. they are neutral) so they are not attracted to the cathode.
Q12a) Because iron is more reactive than copper.
b) No, because iron is less reactive than aluminium so it wouldn't be able to push the aluminium out and bond to the sulfate.
Q13 Any two from, e.g. there is a limited supply of copper. There is an increasing demand for copper. Mining new copper is damaging to the environment.
Q14a) Bioleaching uses bacteria to separate copper from copper sulfide. The bacteria get energy from the bond between copper and sulfur, separating out the copper from the ore in the process. The leachate (the solution produced by the process) contains copper, which can be extracted, e.g. by filtering.
b) Phytomining.
c) The supply of copper-rich ores is limited and the demand for copper is growing. These alternative methods can extract copper from low-grade ores and from the waste that is currently produced when copper is extracted.

Page 70 — Impacts of Extracting Metals

Q1 Social factors include: new jobs available for locals, improved local services, influx of people might put strain on local services.
Economic factors include: more money in local economy, more goods made from the extracted metal are available.
Environmental factors include: pollution such as dust, noise and emissions from vehicles, habitat destruction, scarring of the landscape, after extraction the area may be turned into a conservation area.
Q2 Aluminium is recycled because it takes a lot of energy to extract it from its ore, so even though it is very common extracting new aluminium is very expensive. Gold is recycled because it is rare and so it's too valuable to throw away.

Page 71 — Properties of Metals

Q1 a) Metal 3 (because it has the best heat conduction, and is strong and resistant to corrosion).
b) Metal 2 (because it is the strongest, isn't too expensive and won't corrode too much). (Accept metal 3.)
c) Metal 1 (because it is most resistant to corrosion so it will last a long time).
Q2 It can be bent to make pipes and tanks, and it doesn't react with water.

Q3 a)

Property	Aluminium	Titanium
Density	**low**	**low**
Strength	low	high
Corrosion resistance	**high**	**high**

b) Titanium (both Ti and Al are corrosion resistant, but it also has to be strong to take a person's weight).

Page 72 — Alloys

Q1 a) A mixture of two or more metals or a mixture of a metal and a non-metal.

b) By adding small amounts of carbon or other metals to the iron.

Q2 a)

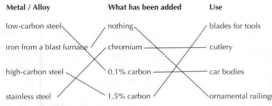

b) It's very brittle.

Q3 37.5% (9 ÷ 24 x 100 = 37.5)

Page 73 — Fractional Distillation of Crude Oil

Q1 a) Crude oil is a **mixture** of different molecules.

b) Most of the compounds in crude oil are **hydrocarbon** molecules.

c) The molecules in crude oil **aren't** chemically bonded to each other.

d) Physical methods **can** be used to separate out the molecules in crude oil.

Q2

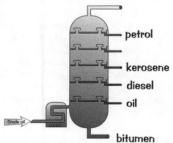

Q3 The larger the molecule the higher the boiling/condensing point.

Q4 The hydrocarbons all have different boiling points. During distillation the oil is heated and the different hydrocarbons boil off at different temperatures. The hydrocarbons can then be condensed individually and the crude oil is successfully separated.

Page 74 — Properties and Uses of Crude Oil

Q1 a)

H   H H   H H H
| | | | | |
H–C–H   H–C–C–H   H–C–C–C–H
| | | | | |
H   H H   H H H
methane   ethane   propane

b) propane

Q2 a) The longer the alkane molecule the **more** viscous (gloopy) it is

b) The shorter the alkane molecule the **lower** its boiling point.

c) The shorter the alkane molecule the **more** flammable it is.

Q3 a) C_nH_{2n+2}

b) $C_{20}H_{42}$ (n = 20 so 2n + 2 = (2 x 20) + 2 = 42)

Q4 a) Oils with long carbon chains are very viscous (gloopy) and so they cling to the moving parts of an engine, preventing damage.

b) Using a hydrocarbon with fewer carbon atoms would be problematic because it would vaporise when the engine got hot / could catch fire easily.

Page 75 — Using Crude Oil as a Fuel

Q1 a) The sun would not always be bright enough to work well / it wouldn't be possible to use solar power at night.

b) The wind wouldn't always be blowing when someone wanted to use the oven.

c) Nuclear substances would be very dangerous if they leaked / it would be very expensive to develop a way of storing the fuel in a safe way.

Q2 New reserves of oil have been discovered since the 1960s. Also, new methods of extraction mean that oil that was once too expensive or difficult to extract can now be used.

Q3 a) When oil is transported by ship there is the possibility of spills into the sea. Crude oil is poisonous to birds and sea creatures.

b) Burning oil products releases carbon dioxide, which causes global warming, and carbon particles (soot) which cause global dimming. The sulfur in oil will make sulfur dioxide which causes acid rain.

Q4 Most technology around today is set up to use crude oil fractions as fuel and converting to alternatives would be time-consuming and costly. We need more energy than can currently be created using alternatives alone. Crude oil fractions are often more reliable than some alternatives, e.g. solar and wind power won't work without the right weather conditions.

Pages 76-77 — Environmental Problems

Q1 The main cause of acid rain is... sulfur dioxide.
Acid rain kills trees and... acidifies lakes.
Sulfur dioxide is produced by burning fuels which contain... sulfur.
Limestone buildings and statues are affected by... acid rain.
In clouds sulfur dioxide reacts with water to make... sulfuric acid.

Q2 Ways of reducing acid rain include:
Removing the sulfur from the fuel before it is burnt (using low-sulfur fuels).
Using scrubbers in power station chimneys to remove sulfur dioxide from emissions.

Q3 a) Carbon monoxide and carbon particles are formed when there is not enough oxygen for a hydrocarbon fuel to burn completely.

b) Carbon monoxide is poisonous.

Chemistry 1a — Products from Rocks

Q4 a) i) false
ii) true
iii) true
iv) false
v) false
b) **Some** fuels produce carbon dioxide when burnt. Oxides of nitrogen form if a fuel burns at **high** temperatures. Soot forms if a fuel **undergoes partial combustion / Sulfur dioxide** forms if a fuel contains sulfur.
Q5 a) hydrocarbon + oxygen → carbon dioxide + water
b) i) Methane: $CH_4 + 2O_2 \rightarrow CO_2 + 2H_2O$
ii) Propane: $C_3H_8 + 5O_2 \rightarrow 3CO_2 + 4H_2O$
Q6 a) hydrocarbon + **oxygen** → water + carbon dioxide + **carbon monoxide + carbon**
b) Because carbon is produced in the form of soot.

Pages 78-81 — More Environmental Problems

Q1 a) The percentage of carbon dioxide in the atmosphere is increasing at an increasing (exponential) rate.
b) The burning of fossil fuels for energy.
c) It's causing the average temperature to increase.
Q2 Global dimming is the reduction in the amount of sunlight reaching the earth's surface. It's thought to be caused by particles of soot and ash produced when fossil fuels are burnt.
Q3 a) water
b) When hydrogen is used as a fuel no carbon dioxide is produced so it doesn't contribute to global warming. It doesn't produce particulates either. Also it doesn't produce sulfur dioxide so it doesn't cause acid rain.
c) Hydrogen-powered vehicles are very expensive because the engines they use are expensive. Hydrogen is difficult to store, which makes it awkward to use as a fuel. Fuelling stations would need to be adapted / converted.
Q4 a) water and carbon dioxide
b) Engines need to be converted before they'll work with ethanol fuels / ethanol fuel isn't widely available.
Q5 $0.9 \times 37\ 000\ 000 =$ **33 300 000 J** or **33.3 MJ**
Q6 a) Answers may include: walking/cycling instead of using vehicles, recycling metals, avoiding foods that have travelled a long way / buying locally produced food, saving electricity by turning lights off, not leaving electrical devices on stand-by, not flying (using other modes of transport that use less fossil fuels), etc.
b) Answer will depend on student's opinion — may argue that everyone who lives on Earth and uses its resources has a responsibility to try and prevent environmental damage. Alternatively, may suggest that new technologies will be able to prevent damage.
Q7 a) When burnt, biodiesel does produce carbon dioxide, but as it comes from recently grown plants which took in this carbon dioxide during their lives it does not increase the net level of the gas in the atmosphere.
b) Normal diesel is produced from crude oil, the remains of dead plants and animals from millions of years ago. When burnt it produces a net increase in the level of atmospheric carbon dioxide.
Q8 a) Recycled cooking oil
b) Climate change might slow down. Spills would be less harmful to the environment.
c) It has reduced the tax on biodiesel and increased the tax on normal diesel.
d) The Government would get less money from fuel tax. It would have to make cuts in other places (e.g. education) or raise the tax on something else.
e) E.g. you don't need to get a diesel car modified. Biodiesel may cost slightly more but the Government is actually making less money on it than it does on normal diesel.

Pages 82-85 — Mixed Questions — Chemistry 1a

Q1 a)

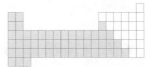

b) The following should be ticked:
Metals are generally strong but also malleable.
Metals conduct electricity well.
Properties of a metal can be altered by mixing it with another metal to form an alloy.
c) R. The material needs to be as light and as strong as possible with a high melting point and a reasonable price. S has a low melting point. T is expensive and fairly dense. U is not very strong and has a high density.
Q2 a) e.g. lubricants/bitumen for surfacing roads.
b) You could get oil spills, which damage the environment.
Q3 a) A finite resource is a resource of which there's a limited amount, which cannot be replenished.
b) i) In general, the more reactive the metal, the later it was discovered.
ii) Less reactive metals are easier to extract from their ores, for example by reduction with carbon. The least reactive metals are sometimes found uncombined in nature. The more reactive metals couldn't be extracted until electricity was discovered to do electrolysis.
c) i) iron(III) oxide + **carbon** → iron + **carbon dioxide**
ii) $2Fe_2O_3 + 3C \rightarrow 4Fe + 3CO_2$
d) i) Electrolysis produces very pure copper which conducts electricity better.
ii) Any two from: easily bent, easily drawn into wires, good conductor of electricity.
e) Aluminium is more reactive than carbon, and so cannot be extracted by reduction with carbon.
Q4 a) The following can be in any order:
Petrol has a lower melting and boiling point than diesel.
Petrol is more flammable (ignites more easily) than diesel.
Petrol is less viscous (flows more easily / is runnier) than diesel.
b) i) E.g. by the fermentation of sugar obtained from plants.
ii) When it's burnt, there are fewer pollutants than from petrol or diesel. / It's carbon neutral because it's made from plants.
Q5 a) Ace oil
b) The viscosity becomes much less.
c) Do the experiment at the average temperature of a car engine.
d) Duncan XYZ oil
Q6

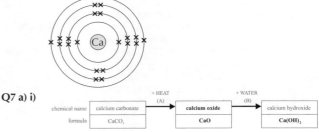

Q7 a) i)

chemical name	calcium carbonate		+ HEAT (A)	calcium oxide		+ WATER (B)	calcium hydroxide
formula	$CaCO_3$			CaO			$Ca(OH)_2$

ii) $CaCO_3 \rightarrow CaO + CO_2$
iii) E.g. neutralising acid soils in fields / acidity in lakes.
b)

Limestone	heat with clay	cement	add sand, water and gravel	concrete

Chemistry 1b — Oils, Earth and Atmosphere

c) Any two of: it doesn't rot when it gets wet; it's cheaper; it's fire resistant; it can't be gnawed away by insects or rodents.

d) cement, sand and water

e) Acid rain reacts with the limestone and causes it to dissolve.

Chemistry 1b — Oils, Earth and Atmosphere

Page 86 — Cracking Crude Oil

Q1 shorter, petrol, diesel, long, high, catalyst, molecules, cracking

Q2 a) E.g. petrol, paraffin, ethene

b) thermal decomposition

Q3 a) ethene

b) 1. The long-chain molecules are heated.
2. They are vaporised (turned into a gas).
3. The vapour is passed over a catalyst at a high temperature.
4. The molecules are cracked on the surface of the catalyst.

Q4 a) kerosene → octane + ethene

b) $C_{10}H_{22} \rightarrow C_8H_{18} + C_2H_4$

Pages 87-88 — Alkenes and Ethanol

Q1 a) C_2H_4

b)

$$H_2C=CH_2$$

c) Propene

d)

$$H_2C=CH-CH_3$$

Q2 a) C_5H_{10}

b) C_6H_{12}

c) C_8H_{16}

d) $C_{12}H_{24}$

Q3 a) False

b) True

c) False

d) True

Q4 bromine water, decolourise, bromine water, orange, colourless

Q5 a) A

b) Method A — Uses yeast.
Method B — Uses a catalyst.

c) Any two of:
Needs lower temperatures so is cheaper. Can use simpler equipment. Uses sugar which is often grown as a major crop. Sugar is a renewable resource.

d) The ethanol produced is not very concentrated/needs to be purified.

Q6 Ethene is a product of crude oil and crude oil is a non-renewable resource. When crude oil starts running out, using ethene to make ethanol will become very expensive.

Pages 89-90 — Using Alkenes to Make Polymers

Q1 The monomer of poly(ethene) is ethene.

Q2 Any three from:
e.g. plastic bags / waterproof coatings for fabrics / tooth fillings / hydrogel wound dressings / memory foam.

Q3 a) Waste remains in landfill. Landfill sites are getting full and more are needed, which takes up useful land.

b) Recycle and reuse.

c) Plastic is currently made from crude oil. As this runs low, its price will rise.

Q4
$$n \left(\begin{array}{c} CH_3\ H \\ | \quad | \\ C=C \\ | \quad | \\ H \quad H \end{array} \right) \longrightarrow \left(\begin{array}{c} CH_3\ H \\ | \quad | \\ C-C \\ | \quad | \\ H \quad H \end{array} \right)_n$$

Q5 Polymers and cornstarch

Q6 Cracking is the breakdown of large molecules into smaller ones, whereas polymerisation is small molecules joining to form bigger molecules.
Cracking makes small alkenes and alkanes, polymerisation often uses alkenes to make alkanes.
Cracking usually involves breaking single bonds between carbon atoms. In polymerisation, the double bonds between carbon atoms are broken.

Pages 91-92 — Plant Oils

Q1 a) Fruits: e.g. avocados and olives
Seeds: e.g. brazil nuts and sesame seeds

b) e.g. food or fuel

c) It squeezes the oil out of the plant material.

Q2 Vegetable oils provide loads of energy, and also contain nutrients.

Q3 a) False

b) True

c) False

d) True

e) False

Q4 a) They provide lots of energy.

b) E.g. biodiesel

Q5 Martin has produced the better method. It is a fair test. He gives accurate quantities. He labels his equipment so there is less opportunity for mistakes.

Q6 a) Reaction with hydrogen with a nickel catalyst at about 60 °C. The double bonds open up and bond to the hydrogen atoms.

b) It increases the melting points of vegetable oils.

c) Some vegetable oils are only partially hydrogenated as turning all the double bonds into single bonds would make the oil too hard. Margarine is an example of this. It is partially hydrogenated so that it is spreadable.

Q7 a) saturated

b) They increase the amount of cholesterol in the blood, which can block arteries and lead to heart disease.

Page 93 — Emulsions

Q1 a) E.g. emulsions can be formed from oil suspended in water or water suspended in oil.

b) E.g. the thicker an emulsion, the more oil it contains.

c) E.g. emulsions can be combined with air and it makes them fluffier.

d) E.g. emulsions are found in foods as well as in non-food items such as moisturisers and paints.

Q2 a)

hydrophobic

hydrophilic

Chemistry 1b — Oils, Earth and Atmosphere

b) Lecithin molecules surround the droplets of oil, with their hydrophilic heads facing out into the water and their hydrophobic tails in the oil droplet. This layer keeps the oil droplets from joining together to separate out from the water.

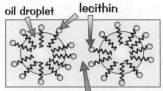

oil droplets can't join together

Q3 a) Emulsifiers increase the shelf-life of food by stopping emulsions from separating out.

b) Some people are allergic to certain emulsifiers, e.g. egg yolk, so they would need to check the ingredients very carefully.

Pages 94-95 — Plate Tectonics

Q1 continental drift, fossils, South America, Africa (alternative pairs of places are possible), land bridges, Pangaea, rotation.

Q2 False, True, True, False, True, False, False, False, True, True

Q3 Fossils of identical plants and animals were found on either side of the Atlantic.
The coastlines of South America and Africa seem to match.
Rocks with matching layers have been found on different continents.
Tropical plant fossils were found in the Arctic islands.

Q4 a) i) Tidal forces and the rotation of the Earth.

ii) The forces would have to be so great that they would stop the Earth from turning, which they hadn't/The forces he proposed were not strong enough.

iii) Any two from: He wasn't a qualified geologist. He had used flawed data. His idea just sounded so strange.

b) The ocean floors and mountains.

Pages 96-97 — The Earth's Structure

Q1 a) $1.6 \times 10\,000 = 16\,000$ cm = **0.16 km**

b) $1.6 \times 20\,000 = 32\,000$ cm = 0.32 km
0.32 km + 325 km = **325.32 km**

Q2 The main earthquake zones are along the plate boundaries.

Q3 A sphere showing 3 layers.
Labels: Crust (outer layer) — very thin, it varies between 5 km and 50 km thickness.
Mantle (next layer down) — properties of a solid but flows very slowly like a liquid. Radioactive decay takes place here.
Core (centre) — mostly iron and nickel.

Q4 Crust — Thinnest of the Earth's layers
Mantle — Slowly flowing semi-solid layer that plates float on
Convection current — Caused by heat from radioactive decay in the mantle
Tectonic plates — Large pieces of crust and upper mantle
Earthquakes — Caused by sudden movements of plates
Volcanoes — Hot spots that often sit on plate boundaries.

Q5 Earthquake: Evidence — Strain in underground rocks.
How reliable is it? — Can only suggest the possibility of an earthquake. Low reliability.
Volcanic eruption: Evidence — Rising molten rock causing the ground to bulge slightly, leading to mini-earthquakes.
How reliable is it? — Molten rock can cool instead of erupting, so not a definite sign. Low/medium reliability.

Pages 98-99 — The Evolution of the Atmosphere

Q1 a) True
b) False
c) True

Q2 The percentage of carbon dioxide has decreased by a large amount because it dissolved into the oceans and a lot of it was converted into limestone from the shells of marine organisms. Plants also used carbon dioxide in the air for photosynthesis.

Q3 The statements should be in this order (from the top of the timeline):
1. The atmosphere is about four-fifths nitrogen and one-fifth oxygen.
2. The build-up of oxygen in the atmosphere allows more complex organisms to evolve and flourish.
The oxygen also creates the ozone layer.
3. Green plants and algae evolve over most of the Earth. They're quite happy in the CO_2 atmosphere. A lot of the CO_2 dissolves into the oceans. The green plants and algae also absorb some of the CO_2 and produce O_2 by photosynthesis.
4. Water vapour condenses to form oceans.
5. The Earth cools down slightly. A thin crust forms. There's lots of volcanic activity.
6. The Earth's surface is molten — it's so hot that any atmosphere just 'boils away' into space.

Q4 a) Largest sector is Nitrogen, second largest is Oxygen, smallest is Carbon dioxide and other gases.

b) Nitrogen: 80% approx (to be more precise, it's 78% in dry air)
Oxygen: 20% approx (to be more precise, it's 21% in dry air)

c) Nitrogen has increased. Carbon dioxide has decreased. Far less water vapour now. Oxygen is now a significant proportion of the atmosphere.

d) As the planet cooled, the water vapour condensed and formed the oceans.

e) Plants and algae photosynthesised and produced it.

f) In any order:
Created the ozone layer which blocked harmful rays from the Sun.
Killed off early organisms/allowed more complex ones to evolve.

Pages 100-101 — Life, Resources and Atmospheric Change

Q1 a) 1. Air is filtered to remove dust.
2. Air is cooled to -200 °C.
3. Carbon dioxide freezes and is removed. Water vapour condenses and is removed.
4. Liquefied air enters the fractionating column and is heated slowly.

b) mixture, boiling points

c) E.g. oxygen, nitrogen.

Q2 a) Billions of years ago, the earth's atmosphere was mainly nitrogen, hydrogen, ammonia and methane.
Lightning struck causing a chemical reaction between these gases and as a result amino acids were formed.
The amino acids collected in a 'primordial soup' — a body of water out of which life gradually crawled.

b) Miller and Urey sealed the gases, nitrogen, hydrogen, ammonia and methane in some apparatus, heated them and applied an electrical charge for a week.

c) Amino acids were created, but not as many as there are on Earth. This suggests that the theory is along the right lines but perhaps not quite right.

Physics 1a — Energy

Q3 a) Burning fossil fuels
b) i) Generally increased, although it has fluctuated.
ii) Global warming
Q4 As the level of CO_2 rises, the amount of CO_2 that the oceans absorb is also rising. The oceans are a natural store of CO_2 but all the extra CO_2 that they are absorbing is making them too acidic. This is causing shellfish and coral to die.

Pages 102-104 — Mixed Questions — Chemistry 1b

Q1 a) There are twice as many hydrogen atoms as there are carbon atoms in each molecule (and no other atoms).
b)

H–C–C=C with H atoms

c) Alkanes only have single bonds, alkenes have a double bond between some carbon atoms. (The general formula of an alkane is C_nH_{2n+2}.)
Q2 a) cracking
b) Ethene can be hydrated with steam to produce ethanol. This requires a high temperature, high pressure and a catalyst.
c) Ethanol can be made by fermentation of sugar. Sugar is obtained from plants which are renewable.
Q3 a) Lots of small molecules (monomers) join up to make long chain molecules (polymers).
b) Name: polystyrene / poly(styrene)

polymer chain structure

c) E.g. it's difficult to get rid of them / they fill up landfill sites.
Q4 a) Any one from:
By crushing rapeseed and then pressing it to extract the oil. / By crushing rapeseed and then using a centrifuge. / By crushing rapeseed and then using a solvent.
b) Rapeseed oil will turn bromine water from orange to colourless.
c) E.g. heart disease.
d) i) An emulsifier stops the oil and water in an emulsion from separating out.
ii) Advantage: Longer shelf life / the food is lower in fat but still has a good texture.
Disadvantage: some people are allergic to some emulsifiers e.g. egg yolk.
Q5 a) E.g. the changes which provided evidence happen very slowly. Technological advances have only recently made it possible to investigate things like the ocean floor.
b) Convection currents in the mantle.
c) Earthquakes and volcanoes
Q6 a) No. It would not support animal life because there is no oxygen. It could support plant life because there is plenty of carbon dioxide for photosynthesis.
b) i) Green plants and algae.
ii) The oceans absorbed CO_2.
c) i) increasing, carbon dioxide, burning
ii) Any one from:
global warming / climate change.
d) i) False, only 1% of the atmosphere is noble gases.
ii) True
iii) False, scientists can't predict volcanoes and earthquakes with any accuracy.

Physics 1a — Energy

Pages 105-106 — Heat Radiation

Q1 a) i) True
ii) True
iii) False
iv) True
v) False
b) Hot objects do absorb infrared radiation.
Cold objects do emit infrared radiation (but much less than hot objects).
Q2 a) Dark, matt surfaces are **good** absorbers and **good** emitters of infrared radiation.
b) The best surfaces for radiating infrared are **good** absorbers and **good** emitters.
c) Silvered surfaces are **poor** absorbers and **poor** emitters of infrared radiation.
d) The best surfaces for solar hot water panels are **good** absorbers and **good** emitters.
Q3 a) Infrared radiation is emitted from the **surface** of hot solid objects **and** from liquids and gases.
b) **All** objects absorb infrared radiation — the bigger the difference in temperature between an object and its surroundings, the **faster** the rate of heat transfer.
Q4 So they lose as little heat energy as possible by radiation (shiny surfaces are poor emitters).
Q5 a) False
b) True
c) True
d) False
e) True
Q6 Flask B will cool fastest because there is a larger temperature difference between the water and the air in the box.
Q7 E.g. Paint the radiator matt black. Put a shiny inner surface between the radiator and the roof. Put a glass (or similar) sheet in front of it. Use a different material for the radiator. Use a bigger radiator. Tilt the radiator so it faces straight at the Sun at noon.

Page 107 — Kinetic Theory

Q1

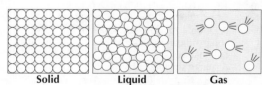
Solid   Liquid   Gas

Gas — There are almost no forces of attraction between the particles.
Liquid — There are weak forces of attraction between the particles.
Solid — There are strong forces of attraction holding the particles close together.
Q2 a) False
b) True
c) True
d) True
e) False
Q3 As you heat a solid, its particles will gain more kinetic energy. They will vibrate more and move faster and eventually overcome the strong forces of attraction that hold the particles in a solid together. Eventually the particles will move fast enough and far enough apart that the substance will become a liquid.

Physics 1a — Energy

Page 108 — Conduction

Q1 a) True
b) False
c) True
d) True
Q2 The piece of wood feels quite warm because wood is a poor conductor, so it does not conduct much heat energy away from George's hand. The metal spoon feels colder because metal is a good conductor, so it conducts heat energy away from his hand very quickly.
Q3 a) Insulator
b) Conductor
c) Conductor
d) Conductor
Q4 a) Copper is a good conductor because it's got free electrons in it. All materials contain electrons, but if they're not free electrons they don't help conduction.
b) Colour and shininess don't make any difference to conduction. Mamphela is getting mixed up with radiation, where it does make a difference.
c) All the particles in all materials have kinetic energy. Ruth doesn't explain that the free electrons mean that kinetic energy is able to move about so easily in copper.

Pages 109-110 — Convection

Q1 a) i) True
ii) False
iii) True
iv) False
b) ii) The colder the water, the denser it is. (Note: this is only true above 4 °C. Below 4 °C, water gets less dense as it cools.)
iv) Convection currents can happen in any liquid or gas.
Q2 The very bottom of a hot water tank stays cold... because water doesn't conduct much heat.
Warm air rises... because it is not so dense.
A small heater can send heat all over a room... because heat flows from warm places to cooler ones.
Q3 a) The particles gain more energy as heat is transferred from the radiator to the air.
b) The particles have more energy so move around faster. The distance between them becomes greater, so the air expands and becomes less dense. This reduction in density means the hotter air rises above the cooler, denser air.

Q4 a)

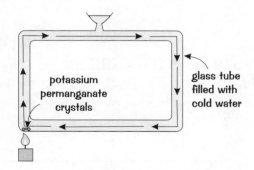

b) The water is heated by conduction.
The temperature of the water increases.
The water expands (as its temperature increases).
The water becomes less dense (as it expands as the particles get further apart).
The warm water floats upwards and is replaced by denser cold water from the right.

Q5 The experiment shows that convection works very well in water — the ice melts because convection currents carry warm water upwards. It also shows that water is a poor **conductor** of heat — convection currents do not warm the water below the flame, and the water below the heater stays cold because conduction only occurs very slowly.

Page 111 — Condensation and Evaporation

Q1 liquid, cools, kinetic energy, attractive.
Q2 a) i) True
ii) False
iii) False
b) ii) Particles can evaporate from a liquid at temperatures much lower than the liquid's boiling point.
iii) The speed of a particle, its mass, the direction it's travelling in and how near the surface it is all affect whether it can escape a liquid.
Q3 Sweating cools you down — when the sweat on your skin evaporates it causes a cooling effect. This is because the fastest particles (the ones with most kinetic energy) are most likely to evaporate from a liquid (the sweat). When they do, the average speed and kinetic energy of the remaining particles decreases. This decrease in average particle energy means the temperature of the remaining liquid falls. Sweating more will increase this cooling effect, as more particles will evaporate from skin.
Q4 a) E.g. if the liquid has a high temperature, low density, large surface area and if there is a low concentration of the liquid in the air it's evaporating into.
b) E.g. if the temperature of the surface the gas touches is lower, if the surface area of the surface the gas touches is larger.

Pages 112-113 — Rate of Heat Transfer

Q1 a) To maximise the amount of heat transfer.
b) Metal is a good conductor so it will conduct heat away from the radiator much faster than air, as air is an insulator.
Q2 Any four from:
Shiny surfaces — reduce radiation.
Insulating foam supports — reduce conduction.
Vacuum gap between walls of bottle — reduce conduction and convection.
Stopper made of poor conductors, e.g. plastic — reduces conduction.
Air space between bottle and outer case — reduces conduction.
Outer case made of plastic — reduces conduction.
Q3 E.g.

	Suggested Improvements
Radiation	Make the outside surface shiny / white / silvery.
Conduction	Cover the tank with 'lagging' material that conducts poorly, e.g. fibreglass.
Convection	Have the tank in a cupboard so warm air can't 'escape', or put a loose cover over it.

Q4 a) The hairs 'stand up' to trap a thicker layer of insulating air around your body to limit the amount of heat lost by convection.
b) Their skin goes pink as the body diverts more blood to flow near the surface of the skin so that more heat can be lost by radiation.
Q5 a) i) Fox A — desert.
ii) Fox B — Arctic.

Physics 1a — Energy

b) Large ears give a large surface area for Fox A to lose heat from easily by radiation. This helps Fox A avoid overheating in a hot climate. Fox B's small ears give a small surface area to minimise heat loss by radiation and stay warm in a cold climate.

Q6 a) Metal is a much better conductor than air because free electrons are able to move and transfer energy easily. Air is an insulator with large gaps between particles. So the metal spoon will conduct heat away from the radiator much faster than air.

b) Radiator B will transfer heat the fastest as a higher proportion of this radiator is in contact with the surroundings. (Its surface area to volume ratio is greater than radiator A.)

Pages 114-115 — Energy Efficiency in the Home

Q1 a) Through the roof — loft insulation.
Through the walls — cavity wall insulation.
Through the doors — double glazing of any glass panels, draught-proofing strips around the frames and letter box.

b) She could install double glazing, fit draught-proofing strips around the windows, and have thick curtains. (Or she could turn her heating down.)

Q2 a) Cavity wall insulation — reduces heat transfer by convection, because pockets of air are trapped in the foam, and can't move between the two walls. The insulation material and trapped air are insulators and so reduce heat transfer by conduction. It also reduces radiation across the gap.

b) Loft insulation — layers of fibreglass wool reduce heat transfer by conduction from the ceiling to the roof space. Heat transfer out of the house by convection is also reduced.

Q3 a) Payback time = 1200 ÷ 20 = **60 years**.

b) No, because although the shutters are cheaper, they are less cost-effective — they have a longer payback time.

Q4 a) U-values measure how effective a material is as an insulator.

b) Gary should choose brand A because it has a lower U-value — the lower the U-value, the better the material is as an insulator, so heat transfer will be less.

Q5 a) Shona is right — a method that pays for itself faster will start saving you money sooner.
Alison is right — good value means getting a good effect from the money spent.
Tim is wrong — cheap or badly installed insulation might not work very well.
Meena is wrong — cost-effectiveness means getting a good energy saving per pound spent.

b) If you plan to move house soon, it makes sense to choose a method with a short payback time. But if you stay in the house for 20 years, say, you would save more in the long term by choosing a method which might cost more to install but gave higher annual savings.

Page 116 — Specific Heat Capacity

Q1 a) Specific heat capacity is the amount of energy needed to raise the temperature of 1 kg of a substance by 1 °C.

b) Substance A

Q2 a) Concrete

b) Water is used because it has a really high specific heat capacity so it can store large amounts of heat, and can be easily pumped around pipes.

Q3 Energy = Mass × SHC × temperature change.
The temperature change for both is 50 °C.
Energy from mercury = 27.2 × 139 × 50 = 189 040 J.

Energy from water = 2 × 4200 × 50 = 420 000 J.
Difference = 420 000 − 189 040 = **230 960 J** (≈ 231 kJ).

Q4 Rearrange the energy equation:
Mass = Energy ÷ (SHC × temperature change).
Mass = 3040 ÷ (380 × 40) = 3040 ÷ 15 200
= **0.2 kg** of copper (or **200 g**).

Pages 117-118 — Energy Transfer

Q1 conservation, transferred, dissipated, created.

Q2 a) **chemical energy** → heat and light energy.

b) electrical energy → **sound and heat energy**.

c) **electrical energy** → **light and heat energy**.

Q3 a) i) chemical energy

ii) heat/thermal energy (and kinetic energy)

b) Any two from:
Chemical energy → heat energy (as the coal burns).
Heat energy → kinetic energy (as the steam drives the engine).
Chemical energy → light energy (in the lamp).
Other answers are possible.

Q4 a) Gravitational potential energy.

b) Chemical energy from the porridge is transferred to kinetic energy in Bruce's muscles and the moving bar. This kinetic energy is then transferred to gravitational potential energy.

c) The gravitational potential energy is transferred into kinetic energy as it falls downwards.

Q5 Electric fan — kinetic energy
Iron — heat energy
Bedside table lamp — light energy

Q6 1. Chemical energy from the archer's food is stored in his muscles.
2. Chemical energy in the archer's muscles is transferred into elastic potential energy.
3. Energy stored in the pulled bow and string is transferred into kinetic energy.
4. As it goes upwards the arrow loses kinetic energy and gains gravitational potential energy.
5. The arrow loses gravitational potential energy and gains kinetic energy as it falls to earth.

Q7 a) In a battery-powered torch, the battery transfers **chemical** energy into **electrical** energy OR the **bulb** transfers electrical energy into light energy.

b) A wind turbine transfers kinetic energy into electrical energy **and heat and sound energy**.

c) A wind-up toy car transfers **elastic potential energy** into kinetic energy and sound energy.

Q8 a) E.g. loudspeaker or buzzer/bell.

b) Solar cell/photovoltaic cell.

c) E.g. hairdryer or electric fan heater.

Pages 119-121 — Efficiency of Machines

Q1 transfer, useful, heat, fraction, input, output.

Q2 a) 100 J

b) 5 J

c) 95 J

Q3

	Total Energy Input (J)	Useful Energy Output (J)	Efficiency
1	2000	1500	**0.75 (or 75%)**
2	**4000**	2000	0.50
3	4000	**1000**	0.25

Q4 Useful power output = efficiency × total power input
= 0.9 × 2000 = **1800 W**.

Physics 1a — Energy

Q5 The winch, like all other devices, is not 100% efficient. 10 J of the 20 J of input energy was 'wasted'. Much of this waste was likely to have been heat energy, generated by friction and electrical resistance in the motor, and between the moving parts of the winch.

Q6 a) By seeing how long each MP3 player can run before the batteries run out. Comparing the times is equivalent to comparing the useful energy outputs (the useful energy output will be proportional to the time).

b) Any two from:
Play the same music, play (the same) music at the same volume, use the same number/type of batteries.

c) Player B is more efficient than player A. In fact player B is one-third more efficient than player A (or player A is only three-quarters as efficient as B).

Q7 A heat exchanger can be used to transfer some of the waste heat energy from the car's engine to the air that's used to warm the passenger compartment.

Q8 a) Any two from:
Longer life.
Cheaper to run OR uses less energy/electricity.
Cheaper to buy per year of its lifetime.
(Or other sensible answers.)

b) Any two from:
Cheaper to buy.
Bright as soon as you switch it on.
Low-energy bulbs can't be used with dimmer switches.
(Or other sensible answers.)

Pages 122-123 — Energy Transformation Diagrams

Q1 a) 10 J.
b) 150 J.
Q2 See diagram below — where the scale is 1 small square = 2 J. Different scales are possible.

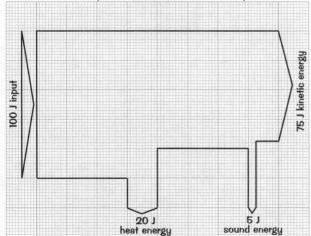

Q3 1. The input energy is not shown clearly.
The 100 J kinetic energy should be shown as input energy.
2. The quantities of energy do not add up. The electrical energy plus the waste heat energy should equal the input energy. Either the input should be 175 J, or the heat wasted should be 25 J. (Or all the values are wrong).

Q4 a) 100 J heat + 40 J GPE = **140 J**
b) 60 J
c) Efficiency = 60 ÷ 200 = **0.3**.

Pages 124-125 — The Cost of Electricity

Q1 a) Energy used = 2 kW × 3 hours = **6 kWh**.
b) Cost of energy = 14p/kWh × 6 kWh = **84p**.
Q2 Energy used = 0.1 kW × 10 h = 1 kWh, so the cost is **11.3p**.
Q3 A 60 W lamp on for 9 h uses 0.06 × 9 = **0.54 kWh**.
An 8 kW shower on for 0.25 h uses 8 × 0.25 = **2 kWh**.
So Tina is right — the shower uses nearly four times as much energy as the lamp.
Q4 a) 34783 − 34259 = **524 kWh**.
b) 524 × 9.7p = 5083p (to nearest penny) = **£50.83**.
Q5 a) Number of kWh used = 7 × 275 × 1000
= 1 925 000 kWh so cost = kWh × night time cost per kWh
= 1 925 000 × 3.7 = 7 122 500p or **£71 225**.
b) kWh generated = 5 × 288 × 1000 = 1 440 000 kWh so cost
= kWh × daytime cost per kWh
= 1 440 000 × 7.2 = 10 368 000 or **£103 680**.
Q6 Difference between meter readings on first night
= 13598.63 − 13592.42 = 6.21 kWh
Difference between meter readings on second night
= 13649.41 − 13646.68 = 2.73 kWh
Difference between energy usage on 1st and 2nd night
= 6.21 − 2.73 = **3.48 kWh**.

Page 126 — Choosing Electrical Appliances

Q1 E.g. It can be used in locations where there is no access to mains electricity. / It's easier to use as there is no power cord to get in the way/restrict movement.

Q2 a) Battery powered lamp: Energy used to fully charge (enough for 8 hours use) = 400 W × 6 hours = 2.4 kWh
Mains powered lamp: Energy used in 8 hours = 1.6 kW × 8 = 12.8 kWh
So, difference in energy used = 12.8 − 2.4 = **10.4 kWh**
b) Difference in cost = 10.4 × 12 = **124.8p**
c) E.g. There might not be an electricity supply where they are camping, so they will not be able to use a mains powered lamp or recharge the battery powered lamp when it runs out. The wind up lamp does not require any electricity to recharge.

Q3 E.g. any two from: can be used to power X-ray machines / refrigeration of medicines/vaccines / can power lighting/ equipment for operations / refrigeration of food.

Pages 127-129 — Mixed Questions — Physics 1a

Q1 a) Pockets of air are trapped in bubbles of foam, reducing convection and radiation across the gap. Air is an insulator, so it also reduces conduction.

b) Paul should look for a low U-value because materials with a low U-value are better insulators, so heat loss will be less.

c) The condensation happens because water vapour in the air cools as it comes into contact with the cold surface. As the vapour cools, the particles in it slow down and lose kinetic energy. The particles no longer have enough kinetic energy to overcome the attractive forces between them, so the vapour becomes a liquid.

Q2 a) E.g.

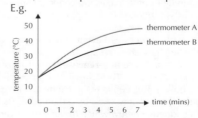

b) The matt black surface is a better absorber of heat radiation (from the Bunsen burner flame) than the shiny silver surface. The matt black surface is also a better emitter of radiation, so the temperature rise for A will be quicker/steeper than for B.

c) chemical energy → heat, light energy and sound energy

Q3 a) The freezer compartment cools the warmer air at the top of the fridge, which then falls, forcing warmer air to rise.

b) Energy (in kWh) = Power (in kW) × Time (in h)
= 0.5 kW × 24 h = 12 kWh.
Cost = No. of units × price per unit
= 12 kWh × 15p = **180p** (= £1.80)

Q4 a) Hot water tank jacket.

b) Over 5 years, the savings would be:
Hot water tank jacket: (5 × £15) – £15 = £60
Draught-proofing: (5 × £65) – £70 = £255
Cavity wall insulation: (5 × £70) – £560 = –£210
Thermostatic controls: (5 × £25) – £120 = £5.
So **draught-proofing** would save the most money.

c) The temperature change required is 36 – 14 = 22 °C.
Energy = mass × SHC × change in temperature
= 90 × 4200 × 22 = **8 316 000 J** (= 8316 kJ = 8.316 MJ).

Q5 a) Chemical energy.

b) E.g. below, using a scale of 1 small square = 25 joules. Other scales are possible.

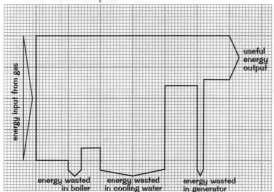

c) Useful output energy = 1000 J – 100 J – 500 J – 50 J = 350 J.
So efficiency = 350 ÷ 1000 = **0.35** (or 35%).

Q6 a) Fins increase the surface area of the heat sink — a larger surface area means they emit heat quickly.

b) i) Metals are good conductors of heat because they have free electrons which can quickly transfer energy.

ii) The free electrons at the hot end move faster and collide with other free electrons, transferring energy. These other electrons then pass on their extra energy to other electrons, and so on across the piece of metal.

Physics 1b — Electricity and Waves

Page 130 — Energy Sources & Power Stations

Q1 1. Coal is burned to release heat.
2. Water is heated in a boiler and turned to steam.
3. Hot steam rushes through a turbine and makes it spin.
4. The spinning turbine makes the generator spin too.
5. Electricity is produced by the spinning generator.

Q2 a) Nuclear fission produces heat.

b) Non-renewable sources will eventually run out / cannot be replaced when they are used up.

Q3 Most power stations use **non-renewable** sources of energy, such as coal, oil or gas. These **fossil** fuels are initially burnt in a boiler. This converts the **chemical** energy in the fuel to **heat** energy. A turbine then converts this energy into **kinetic** energy, which, in turn, is converted to **electrical** energy by a generator. This energy feeds into the national grid ready to be distributed to consumers.

Q4 Wind and solar power are unreliable as they depend on appropriate weather conditions to generate power. Whereas fossil fuels can be burnt all the time.

Page 131 — Renewable Energy Sources (1)

Q1 a) Any three from: they make a lot of noise, they spoil the view/landscape / cause visual pollution, they harm wildlife / they kill birds, they only work if it's windy, the electricity they generate is expensive, a lot of turbines are needed to replace one power station.

b) Any three from: once running, there's no permanent damage to the landscape, they use a renewable, free source of energy, running costs are low, they don't release greenhouse gases into the atmosphere.

Q2 Disadvantages — the initial costs are high, and most solar cells are not very efficient, they don't work well when it's cloudy. Advantages — they use a renewable and free source of energy (there are no fuel costs), they are a good way to provide energy in remote places, there is no pollution when they are in use.

Q3 a) They're a good source of energy in situations where only a small amount of electricity is needed, e.g. calculators. They're often available in places where there is no access to mains electricity, e.g. remote road signs.

b) The cost of connecting the remote farm to the National Grid would be enormous compared with the value of the electricity generated.

Pages 132-133 — Renewable Energy Sources (2)

Q1 a) Measurements provide more information than observations. The voltage gives a more accurate idea of how much energy was transferred.

b) Their results **do not support** their prediction because the relationship is not proportional — e.g. halving the height (200 cm to 100 cm) does not halve the voltage (0.2 V is not half of 1.1 V).

Q2 1. At night big power stations make more electricity than is needed.
2. Spare electricity is used to pump water from reservoirs at a low level to others at a high level.
3. Water at a high level stores energy until it is needed.
4. At peak times, when demand is the highest, water is allowed to flow downhill, powering turbines and generating electricity.

Q3 Big coal-fired power stations deliver energy... all the time. Pumped storage power stations deliver energy... that they have previously stored / when it is needed. Hydroelectric power stations deliver electricity... when it is needed.

Q4 a) The student could say that no atmospheric pollution is produced when electricity is being generated, or that building the dams and manufacturing the turbines, generators etc. does cause atmospheric pollution/or that the power plant will cause both visual and noise pollution.

b) The student could say that there are no fuel costs, or that building dams and purchasing turbines etc. is expensive.

c) The student might argue that dams are unsightly, they disturb the natural environment, and disrupt / destroy wildlife habitats etc., or they could argue that an impressive engineering structure has a positive visual impact, and/or that not all hydroelectric projects involve building dams.

Physics 1b — Electricity and Waves

d) The student could say that it is rare for reservoirs to be empty even in dry weather, and water can be released to power the generators when it's needed most, or they could say that power supplies are less reliable during droughts, and this may be a more serious problem in the future.

e) Any two from: it is a renewable source of energy, it does not contribute to global warming (once running), the output can be varied more quickly than that of most other power stations, good for use in remote locations.

f) Any two from: rotting vegetation releases greenhouse gases (methane and CO_2) when the valley is flooded, set-up costs are high, set-up times are long, destruction of wildlife habitats.

Page 134 — Renewable Energy Sources (3)

Q1 a) Tidal.
b) Wave.
c) Tidal.
d) Wave.
e) Tidal.

Q2 a) When the tide comes in the water passes through the turbines and then builds up behind the barrage. When the tide goes out the water is allowed out through the turbines in the barrage at a controlled speed. As the water passes through the turbines electricity is generated. (The water also turns the turbines on the way in.)

b) Any two from the following: Initial costs are fairly high. Barrages can look unattractive. Barrages can prevent access for boats. Barrages can damage habitats. The height of tides is variable. No energy is available at the turn of the tides.

Q3 a) 1. A wave moves water upwards, forcing air out towards a turbine.
2. The moving air makes the turbine spin.
3. The spinning turbine drives a generator.
4. The spinning generator makes electricity.
5. The water goes down again.
6. Air is sucked downwards, spinning the turbine the other way and generating more power.

b) Any two from the following: High initial costs. Spoiling the view. Can be unreliable because it depends on winds. It is currently only suitable for small-scale use. Can be a hazard to boats.

Page 135 — Renewable Energy Sources (4)

Q1 Biofuels are used to generate electricity in a similar way to **fossil fuels**. Biofuels are burnt to heat **water** and make **steam**, which is used to drive **turbines** to power generators and make electricity.
Biofuels can be solids (e.g. **woodchips**), liquids (e.g. **ethanol**) or gases (e.g. **methane**).

Q2 In some volcanic areas, hot water and steam rise to the surface. This steam can be used to drive turbines to generate electricity.

Q3 Biofuels will not run out — more can always be made to us as a source of energy.

Q4 a) False
b) False
c) False
d) True

Page 136 — Energy Sources and the Environment

Q1 Acid rain... sulfur dioxide formed by burning oil and coal. Climate change... releasing CO_2 by burning fossil fuels. Dangerous radioactive waste... using nuclear power. Spoiling of natural landscapes... coal mining OR sulfur dioxide formed by burning oil and coal.

Q2 Answer will depend on student's opinion but should include an explanation of their reasoning, e.g. Lisa because nuclear power produces long-lasting, dangerous, radioactive waste.
Or Ben because nuclear power is carefully controlled to reduce any dangers. Also, nuclear power doesn't produce any carbon dioxide, whereas using fossil fuels adds to the carbon dioxide in the atmosphere, leading to climate change / an increased greenhouse effect / global warming.

Q3 Plants that are used to produce biofuels (or to feed animals that produce biofuels) absorb carbon dioxide from the atmosphere. Burning the biofuel puts the carbon back into the atmosphere as carbon dioxide, so overall there is a neutral effect on the atmosphere.

Q4 a) This is the process of collecting carbon dioxide from power stations before it is released into the atmosphere.
b) E.g. in empty gas fields, oil fields, dissolved in seawater at the bottom of the ocean, capturing with algae.

Pages 137-138 — Comparison of Energy Resources

Q1 Gas

Q2 a) Any one of: gas supplies often need to be imported and there may be steep price rises, gas will run out eventually, burning gas causes atmospheric pollution and contributes to the global warming.
Other answers are possible.

b) Any one of: high set-up costs, high maintenance and/or decommissioning costs, long set-up times, dangerous radioactive waste, risk of catastrophic accidents, threat from terrorism, nuclear fuels need to be imported.
Other answers are possible.

c) Any one of: it's dependent on the weather / only works when the wind is blowing, unreliable, visual pollution / spoils the view, noise pollution. Other answers are possible.

d) E.g. high set-up costs. Other answers are possible.

Q3 a) Most (about 75%) of the UK's electricity generation depends on supplies of coal, oil and gas. These fuels are all non-renewable and will run out eventually.

b) 1. We don't know how to dispose of the radioactive waste safely.
2. Nuclear power stations and radioactive waste are targets for terrorists.

c) Shutting down / removing from active status.

d) Answer will depend on student's opinion. 'I agree' could be backed up by mentioning that sea levels change in a predictable and reliable way, twice every day, and/or that the UK has a long coastline and plenty of opportunities to use the resource. 'I disagree' could be backed up by saying that there are only a few suitable estuaries, or that at neap tides, the difference in sea level between low and high tides is small, so there is not much energy available.

e) E.g. Any two from: it's a reliable source of energy, it doesn't release greenhouse gases, we're not likely to run out of uranium any time soon (and some of the waste can be reprocessed and reused).

Physics 1b — Electricity and Waves

Pages 139-140 — Electricity and the National Grid

Q1
1. Electrical energy is generated in power stations.
2. The voltage of the supply is raised.
3. An electrical current flows through power cables across the country.
4. The voltage of the supply is reduced.
5. Mrs Miggins boils the kettle for tea.

Q2 a) Underground cables
b) Overhead cables
c) Overhead cables
d) Overhead cables
e) Underground cables
f) Overhead cables
g) Underground cables

Q3 a) Step-up transformer, pylons, step-down transformer, insulators.
b) At higher voltages, less energy is wasted as heat. This saves more money than the cost of the equipment.

Q4 a) The National Grid transmits energy at high voltage and **low current**.
b) A step-up transformer is used to **increase** the voltage of the supply (OR reduce the **current**) before electricity is transmitted.
c) Using a **low current** (OR high **voltage**) makes sure there is not much energy wasted.

Q5 a) Supply is the amount of electricity generated and delivered to consumers. Demand is the amount of electricity needed by the consumers.
b) Consumer demand for energy is increasing, so the National Grid has to increase the supply to meet this demand.
c) E.g. More plants can be built, power output of power plants can be increased.
d) E.g. Use energy efficient appliances, being more careful not to waste energy in the home (e.g. by turning off lights).

Pages 141-142 — Wave Basics

Q1 energy, matter
Q2 a) Transverse — 2, Longitudinal — 1.
b) E.g. transverse waves can travel in a vacuum but longitudinal waves cannot / vibrations in a transverse wave are perpendicular to the direction of energy transfer, whereas in longitudinal waves they are parallel to the direction of energy transfer.

Q3 a) A and C
b) A and B
c) A and C

Q4 Transverse
vibrations are at 90° to the direction of energy transfer
produced by a slinky spring whose end is wiggled at 90° to the spring itself
ripples on water
electromagnetic radiation
Longitudinal
vibrations are along the same direction as the energy transfer
sound waves
produced by a slinky spring whose end is pushed and pulled towards and away from the rest of the spring

Q5 a) metres
b) There are 25 waves per second.
c) A

Q6

Q7 You need to work out the frequency.
Using $v = f\lambda$ and rearranging gives
frequency = speed ÷ wavelength.
So frequency = $(3 \times 10^8) \div (5 \times 10^{-7}) = \mathbf{6 \times 10^{14}\,Hz}$.

Q8 a) He has drawn a wave with a wavelength of 4 m rather than 2 m.
b)
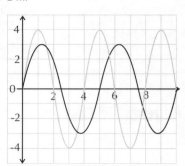

Q9 You need to work out the wavelength.
Using $v = f\lambda$ and rearranging gives:
wavelength = speed ÷ frequency.
So wavelength = $(3 \times 10^8) \div (4.6 \times 10^{15}) = \mathbf{6.5 \times 10^{-8}\,m}$

Page 143 — Wave Properties

Q1 a) The normal is an imaginary line that's at right angles to the surface at the point of incidence (where the light hits the surface).
b)
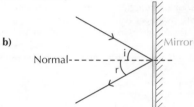

Q2 a)
 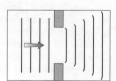
b) virtual
c) upright
d) The left and right hand side of the object are swapped round in the image. E.g. the right hand side of the actual pencil appears to be the left hand side of the pencil on the image.

Page 144 — Refraction and Diffraction

Q1 a) Diffraction is the spreading out of waves when they pass through a gap or past an obstacle.
b)

Q2 a) B
b) Waves don't refract when they're travelling along the normal.
c) When a wave changes direction as it hits the boundary between two different media.

Q3 The gap is too wide. The gap needs to be of similar magnitude (size) to the wavelength of the wave.

Physics 1b — Electricity and Waves

Pages 145-146 — EM Waves and Communication

Q1 a)

Radio waves	Micro-waves	Infrared			Ultraviolet	X-rays	Gamma rays
1m-10^{-1}m	10^{-2}m (1 cm)	10^{-5}m (0.01mm)		10^{-7}m	10^{-8}m	10^{-10}m	10^{-15}m

b) The energy of the waves **increases** from **left to right** across the table.

Q2 a) i) False
ii) False
iii) False
iv) True

b) i) Visible light travels **at the same speed** in a vacuum **as both** X-rays and radio waves.
ii) All EM waves transfer **energy** from place to place.
iii) Radio waves have the **longest** wavelength of all EM waves.

Q3 A, B and C

Q4 EM waves with higher frequencies have **shorter** wavelengths.
The **higher** the frequency of an EM wave, the greater the energy of the wave.

Q5 The house can receive **long-wave** signals because they can diffract around the mountain. It also receives **short-wave** signals because they are reflected by the **ionosphere**. However **FM** signals are not received at the house as the transmitter is not in direct line of sight of the house.

Q6 Things they have in common — any two from: they can both travel in a vacuum, they both travel at the speed of light, they both transfer energy.
(Or other sensible answers.)
Ways in which they differ — any two from: they have different wavelengths, they have different frequencies, they have different energies.
(Or other sensible answers.)

Pages 147-148 — EM Waves and Their Uses

Q1 Infrared

Q2 a) This allows the satellite to send signals to (and receive signals from) a large area of the Earth.
b) Radio waves can't pass easily through the earth's watery atmosphere.
c) Microwaves

Q3 a) Visible light or infrared waves.
b) They are reflected down the core of the fibre.

Q4 The microwaves are not absorbed or reflected much by the water molecules in clouds (unlike visible light).

Q5 a) Microwaves
b) Their brain cells may be heated up and damaged.
c) E.g. convenience (e.g. keeping in touch with friends), safety (they feel the positives outweigh the risks).
Also many people only use their phones for short periods of time, so they have limited exposure.

Q6 E.g. The lens focuses the light onto a light sensitive film or electronic sensor. The film or sensor then records the image.

Pages 149-150 — Sound Waves

Q1 C, A, D, B.
Q2 vibrate, high, low.
Q3 The bigger the **amplitude** of a sound wave, the **louder** the sound.
Q4 2000
Q5 a) 30 Hz
b) 5 Hz, 630 Hz, 8 kHz, 21 kHz, 400 kHz, 3 MHz
Q6 a) A reflected sound wave.
b) The soft surfaces in her bedroom absorb the sound vibrations better, so less sound is reflected around the room.

c) The echoed sound has to travel further, and so takes longer to reach your ears.

Q7 a) It gets quieter and eventually stops. Because sound is a vibration passed from molecule to molecule, it cannot be transmitted through a vacuum.
b) The foam prevents the sound from being transmitted through the solid surface that the clock is placed on.

Pages 151-152 — The Origin of the Universe

Q1 a) It will sound lower pitched.
b) Doppler effect
c) The wavelength seems to increase.
d) The frequency would seem to have increased.

Q2 As the train leaves, it moves away from Brian's microphone. So the frequency appears to get slightly **lower**. E.g.

Q3 Light from other galaxies is red-shifted — all the frequencies are lower in the spectrum than is the case for other objects nearby. This tells us that the galaxies are moving away from us. Also, the further away the galaxy, the greater the red-shift. This tells us that more distant galaxies are moving away from us at a faster rate than nearer galaxies.

Q4 a) The universe started as a single point that exploded in the Big Bang and has been expanding ever since.
b) Space itself is expanding.

Q5 a) Low frequency electromagnetic radiation coming from all parts of the universe.
b) Very shortly after the beginning of the universe, the universe was very hot and emitted very high energy, high frequency radiation. As the universe expanded it cooled, and this radiation dropped in frequency and is now detected as the CMBR.

Q6 E.g. Any one from: It can't explain observed acceleration and expansion of the universe. / It doesn't tell you anything about the universe before the Big Bang.

Pages 153-156 — Mixed Questions — Physics 1b

Q1 a) B represents ultraviolet radiation.
The infrared wave has the largest amplitude.
b) B — They are all transverse waves.
D — They all travel at the same speed in space.

Q2 a) i) E.g. Solar cells require little maintenance and no fuel, making them suitable for remote locations (where transporting fuel and arranging repairs would be difficult and expensive). Solar power is a renewable source of energy and won't pollute the island.
ii) E.g. The island is likely to be quite windy. Wind turbines are fairly cheap to install. As with solar power, wind power is renewable, doesn't cause pollution and doesn't require fuel.
b) Wave power — around the coastline, biomass — llama poo could be used to produce biofuel for burning. (Hydroelectric power might also be possible, depending on the island's geography and climate.)

Q3 a) Frequency = speed ÷ wavelength = 3×10^8 m/s ÷ 1500 m = **200 000 Hz** (= 200 kHz).
b) Longer waves diffract more around large objects than shorter waves. So the long-wave radio signal diffracts around the mountains and can be received in Mr Potts' holiday cottage. The TV signal is short-wave so it doesn't diffract much and can't be received in his cottage.

Physics 1b — Electricity and Waves

Q4 a) E.g. it's clean / fuel is relatively cheap / it's reliable

b) Carbon capture and storage technology is used to collect CO_2 from fossil-fuel power stations before it is released into the atmosphere. This reduces the amount of CO_2 building up in the atmosphere and reduces the strength of the greenhouse effect.

Q5 a) reflection

b)

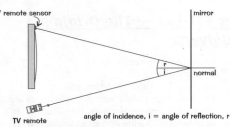

angle of incidence, i = angle of reflection, r

Q6 a) The 'spare' electricity can be used to pump water up to a higher reservoir, which can then be released quickly during periods of peak demand to generate electricity.

b) E.g. increase supply by opening more power plants, increase supply by increasing the power output of power plants, consumers reducing their demands.

Q7 a) Diffraction

b) It will diffract the most when the gap is the same size as the wavelength. If the gap is much wider than the wavelength, it will only diffract a little.

c) Water molecules can absorb some wavelengths of microwave. If the water in question happens to be in your cells, e.g. brain cells, this may cause cell damage / your brain might start to cook.

Q8 a) 0.02 m

b) 10 Hz

c) speed = wavelength × frequency
$= 0.02 × 10 =$ **0.2 m/s**

Q9 a) The gas is burned to convert its stored chemical energy into heat energy. The heat is used to turn water into steam, which drives turbines. Generators then convert the kinetic energy of the turbine blades into electrical energy.

b) i) nuclear energy, biofuel

ii) Both solar and wind power are unreliable / dependent on the weather. / On days which weren't sunny or windy, there would be little or no electricity.

c) i) So that the current required to transmit power can be low, which reduces the energy wasted through heating in the cables.

ii) The high voltage is 'stepped down' using a series of transformers before it reaches people's homes or businesses.

Q10 a)

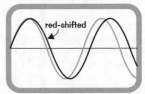

b) More distant galaxies have greater red-shifts than nearer ones, showing that more distant galaxies are moving away from us faster. This is evidence that the universe is expanding and started in a very dense (and hot) state.

ISBN 978 1 84146 707 8

9 781841 467078

SAHA45